Robbie Williams
Intensive Care

PIANO/VOCAL/GUITAR

www.robbiewilliams.com

Wise Publications, part of The Music Sales Group
London/New York/Paris/Sydney/Copenhagen/Berlin/Madrid/Tokyo

COME

EITHER  NEITHER

GO

BELOVED

EITHER  NEITHER

FORGOTTEN

SACRIFICE

EITHER  NEITHER

SELF - LOVE

FIGHT

EITHER 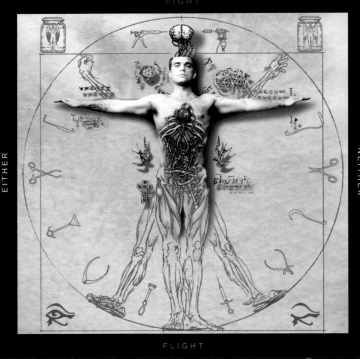 NEITHER

FLIGHT

EITHER INSPIRED NEITHER

INSANE

EITHER PAST NEITHER

FUTURE

TRUTH

EITHER NEITHER

LIES

MYSTERY

EITHER NEITHER

REVELATION

Published by

Wise Publications, 8/9 Frith Street, London,
W1D 3JB, England.

Exclusive Distributors

Music Sales Limited, Distribution Centre,
Newmarket Road, Bury St Edmunds, Suffolk,
IP33 3YB, England.

Publishing Details

Order No. AM984533
ISBN: 1-84609-317-1
This book © Copyright 2005 Wise Publications,
a division of Music Sales Limited.

Management: ie:music ltd

Music arranged by Derek Jones and Jack Long.
Music processed by Paul Ewers Music Design.
Tarot concept, design and artwork Grant
Morrison and Frank Quitely.
Printed in the United Kingdom.

Your Guarantee of Quality

As publishers, we strive to produce every
book to the highest commercial standards.

The music has been freshly engraved to
make playing from it a real pleasure.

Particular care has been given to specifying
acid-free, neutral-sized paper made from
pulps which have not been elemental chlorine
bleached. This pulp is from farmed sustainable
forests and was produced with special regard
for the environment.

Throughout, the printing and binding have been
planned to ensure a sturdy, attractive publication
which should give years of enjoyment.

If your copy fails to meet our high standards,
please inform us and we will gladly replace it.

www.musicsales.com

Ghosts

Words & Music by R. Williams/S. Duffy

11

Tripping

Words & Music by R. Williams/S. Duffy

14

Make Me Pure

Words & Music by R. Williams/S. Duffy

song I've sung be-fore and a song I'm gon-na sing____ a - gain.____
no one else is laugh-ing then why am I?____
stand-ing for e - lect - tion all a - cross the known u - ni - verse.____

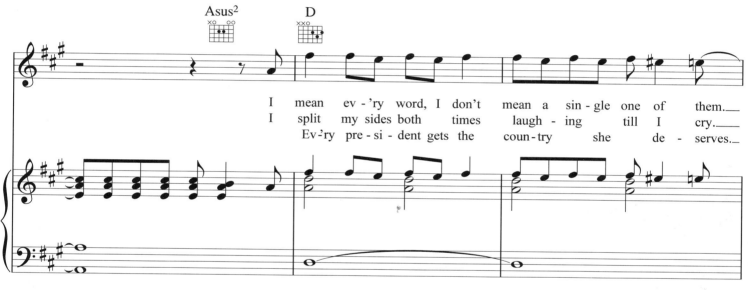

I mean ev -'ry word, I don't mean a sin-gle one of them.____
I split my sides both times laugh - ing till I cry.____
Ev-'ry pre - si - dent gets the coun-try she de - serves.__

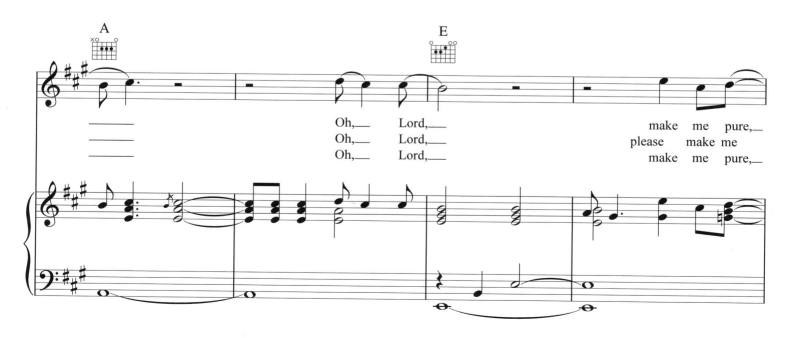

____ Oh,___ Lord,___ make me pure,__
____ Oh,___ Lord,___ please make me
____ Oh,___ Lord,___ make me pure,__

all   for you.___   I'm not

per - fect,   but you don't mind that,   do   you?___

I know you're there___   to pull___ me   through.___   Aren't   you?

D.S. al Coda

___ 5. So   I   look   for   love,_

⊕ Coda

but not   yet.___

23

Spread Your Wings

Words & Music by R. Williams/S. Duffy

1. I used to live 'round here   I was the boy with   flash clothes.
2. So she walks into this dead-end bar,   sticks her handbag   on the chair.
3. Now she loves somebody else   in   flash clothes.

She was the girl with the acid stare.   I saw her at The Place.   You know she knows you know.
So she walks into this   dead-end bar,   puts her handbag   on the chair.
She was the girl with the acid stare.   And now she paid to have one of those.

Advertising Space

Words & Music by R. Williams/S. Duffy

1. There's no earth - ly way____ of know - ing what was
2. Through your eyes____ the world____ was burn - ing.

in your heart____ when it stopped go - ing. The whole world shook,____ a
"Please be gen - tle, I'm____ still learn - ing", you seemed to say,____ as

storm was blow - ing through.____ you.
you kept turn - ing up.____ They

Wait - ing for____ God to stop____ this and
poi - soned you____ with com - pro - mise, at

Please Don't Die

Words & Music by R. Williams/S. Duffy

1. Let me lie down, please don't wake me.
2. Take me dancing, I love music.

Nothing's sacred and no-one saved me.
Keep on singing, we won't lose it.

Your Gay Friend

Words & Music by R. Williams/S. Duffy

A - no - ther friend to_____ have a go on._____
And make sure that he nev - er hears this song._____

And she asks_____
And she says_____

_____ me do_____ I miss her when_ she's gone._____
_____ that I'm_ the op - po - site of a Hall - mark card.

And I_____ re - ply_____ "As much as I_____ miss
She asks_____ me how_ I'm feel - ing. Well, I

41

44

45

Sin Sin Sin

Words & Music by R. Williams/S. Duffy

1. Don't let your eyes tell the brain. You should feel a-shamed. Ev-'ry-one needs

it, ba - by, and I feel the same.

Did-n't quite catch your name.

(1.)Hush, hush, hush, don't say a thing.
(2.) Just re - lax, it's what Je - sus would do.

Let's see what the night will bring,
We're made in his i - mage, ba - by,

47

Random Acts Of Kindness

Words & Music by R. Williams/S. Duffy

Hap-py Christ-mas and New Year, I raise_ a toast_____ to you.

And if it hurts_____ to be_ so blind,_____ why don't you try_

_____ be - ing_____ kind?_____

2. They've de - cid - ed
3. I am just_ a

54

I pray_ you'll find_ where you be - long._ All the words_

_ I have_ re - pressed_ are com-ing out_ to - day,_ I guess._

_ It's jus - tice, not_ re - spect_ I'm af - ter, and

that just means con - tempt_ for you_

The Trouble With Me

Words & Music by R. Williams/S. Duffy

there's no trou-ble with you.___

So when you say that you love___ me, that stops me lov-ing you.___

D.S. al Coda

⊕ *Coda*

woh, yeah, yeah, yeah;_____ woh,_ woh,_

A Place To Crash

Words & Music by R. Williams/S. Duffy

Love_____ me like_____ I'm cash._____

You_____ can { feel_____ / see_____ } the class._____

2. If, if, if, if, if there's a Ah._____

Ah._____

Kiss me_____ with your mouth._____
Teach me_____ with your brain._____

Ah, oh._____

69

King Of Bloke And Bird

Words & Music by R. Williams/S. Duffy

123456789